MAID

AND

HER MERRY MEN

How the Band Got Together

Tony Robinson

HIT PLAYS

THE FWOG PWINCE by Kaye Umansky
BILL'S NEW FROCK by Anne Fine
THE COMPUTER NUT by Betsy Byars
COLLISION COURSE by Nigel Hinton
MAID MARIAN AND HER MERRY MEN
by Tony Robinson

Series Editors

Robin Little
Patrick Redsell
Erik Wilcock

CONTENTS

This episode was first broadcast on BBC Television in 1989 and was produced by Richard Callanan.

Introduction

Maid Marian and Her Merry Men –'How the Band Got Together' by Tony Robinson is one of the books in **Hit Plays**. All of the titles in the series have been produced for either television or radio.

The plays are very much in the form they were in when they were first recorded. This play relies quite heavily on camera directions and these have been edited so that they can be spoken dramatically by two narrators.

The plays in the series are for readers aged 11–13. This does not mean that all of them are the same in any way; they are as varied as the people who will study them as part of their reading programme for Key Stage 3 in English. The one thing the plays have in common is that they are enjoyable to read.

On the next page you will find a section entitled 'What the play is about'. This summarises the action in the play as well as focusing on some of the main issues dealt with in it. Following this, there is a section called 'Preparing for reading'. This gives the information you need to read the play successfully. There are brief descriptions of the characters, who they are and how much they have to say.

At the end of the book there are two sections which outline some activities you can do after you have read the play. 'Drama activities' (page 39) provides clearly organised ways of getting to grips with the script and how it works in production. 'Writing and talking about the play' (page 41) gives some straight-forward assignments to help you in your understanding of the play.

What the play is about

The peasants in Worksop Village don't enjoy themselves very much. Not only are they persecuted by the Sheriff of Nottingham and his men, they are surrounded by mud, they are covered in mud and worse still, they have nothing to eat and drink but mud. They clearly need someone to fight for their rights and set them free, but who could it be?

On her way to Worksop Market to sell her pet tadpole, Edwina, Maid Marian meets Little Ron, the guardian of the bridge. Of course, she has no trouble in beating him in single combat. At the market, she meets Robin, a cowardly but very trendy tailor, who has just completed a large pair of underpants for King John.

The Sheriff of Nottingham is there too, enjoying himself throwing tomatoes at the unfortunate Rabies, who has just been thrown into the stocks. When one of the tomatoes accidentally hits Maid Marian, she retaliates by throwing the barrel that she is carrying straight at the Sheriff. It contains not only water, but her pet, Edwina. In the ensuing fracas, Edwina is first swallowed by the Sheriff, then goes up Rabies' nose.

Maid Marian escapes by the skin of her teeth, kidnapping Robin and the Royal underpants. Whilst making their escape, the pair meet Little Ron again. Maid Marian realises that they must now live the life of outlaws, dedicated to freeing their country from injustice. Robin is much less enthusiastic, even about their first important mission, which is clearly to free Edwina, now trapped up Rabies' nose in the Sheriff of Nottingham's castle . . .

In this farcical comedy, Tony Robinson turns the legend of Robin Hood on its head, by giving the role of the brave freedom fighter to Maid Marian. Through a whole series of ridiculous but hilarious situations, he creates an extremely enjoyable and readable play. Although it is obviously not intended to be taken seriously, the play contains many interesting opportunities for responding to the language, the dramatic devices and the ideas that it contains.

Preparing for reading

This play is written in very straightforward yet humorous language and should not present too many problems. There are fourteen speaking parts: two females, nine males, one tadpole and two narrators. The narrators are used to set the scene and describe characters' thoughts, feelings and reactions to events. They have the two largest speaking parts. At the end of the play there is a gospel choir – the entire class or group could sing this part. At the beginning of each scene, the characters who appear in it are listed.

The action of the play takes in a variety of locations and covers a time span of one day. Since the play is a spoof based on a

Character	Description	Role
NARRATOR 1	narrator	large
NARRATOR 2	narrator	large
MARIAN	the heroine	large
ROBIN	boutique keeper	large
BARRINGTON	minstrel and entrepreneur	medium
RABIES	peasant	small
LITTLE RON	bridge keeper	medium
THE SHERIFF	villain	large
KING JOHN	another villain	small
GARY	Norman soldier	small
GRAEME	Norman soldier	small
GATEKEEPER	gatekeeper	small
EDWINA	tadpole	small
OLD LADY	peasant (Gladys)	small

well-known story, Robin Hood, the language, ideas and humour should be easily recognisable to most pupils.

This play can be read around the class in a couple of sessions. The roles of the narrators are very important and their lines should be read dramatically. They can really heighten the dramatic situations and contain a good deal of humour.

The play can also be read in groups of five or six. There are never more than eight characters in one scene. As long as the readers for Narrators 1 and 2 remain constant the others can negotiate the rest of the reading themselves on a scene-by-scene basis.

To get you started

Before you start reading this play here is an issue that you might like to discuss.

The play you are about to read is called a spoof. This means that it takes a well-known story or format and then changes it so that it becomes funny. The title of the play is a clue to one of the major changes in the story: Maid Marian is the leader, not Robin Hood.

First discuss what you know about the Robin Hood legend and what you would expect of a play entitled *Robin Hood and His Merry Men.*

Next discuss any spoofs that you may have seen on television or video or read in a magazine, and describe any scenes or sections of these spoofs which you have found amusing, giving your reasons.

Maid Marian and Her Merry Men

How the Band Got Together

Scene 1: Worksop village

(NARRATORS 1 and 2, BARRINGTON, OLD LADY, RABIES, SHERIFF and MARIAN)

NARRATOR 1 This is Worksop village; a few tatty huts surrounded by scenes of disgusting, revolting and extremely muddy squalor.

BARRINGTON Mud! Mud!
All over the street
It sticks to your feet it's
Mud! Mud!
You get it in your hair
You get it everywhere, that
Mud! Brown mud!

There's a mad, bad king and he's called
  King John
And he sits on a big bad throne
And he takes all the people's money
And he won't leave the people alone.
He taxes their farms. He taxes their homes.
He taxes their flesh and blood.
He lives for the pleasure of counting his
  treasure
But all that the people gotta eat is . . .

NARRATOR 2 An old lady peasant slams a huge covered plate onto a table.

OLD LADY Mud!

NARRATOR 1 She lifts the cover revealing a huge pile of mud.

BARRINGTON Mud!

NARRATOR 2	The faces of her family are glum. She sees a blue-bottle on the mud, produces a fly-swatter, and thwacks the mud pie, splattering the family's faces with mud.
BARRINGTON	They eat mud pies That are covered in flies, just . . . Mud! Sweet Mud!
NARRATOR 2	A child with bread in one hand, takes a huge dollop of mud and spreads it on the bread.
BARRINGTON	They make mud spread. And they spread it on their bread, that's . . . Mud! Just Mud!
NARRATOR 1	A peasant drinks from a tankard, then blows a stream of mud into the face of another peasant.
BARRINGTON	They drink, then they cry 'Here's mud in your eye', that's . . . Mud!
NARRATOR 2	Enter Rabies, a large, but totally pathetic peasant who makes Winnie the Pooh seem an intellectual giant. He is completely bald save for a top-knot and a fringe.
BARRINGTON	Mud!
RABIES	Raffle tickets!
BARRINGTON	Mud!

RABIES	Who will buy a raffle ticket? Fabulous prizes!
NARRATOR 1	The Sheriff of Nottingham enters. He is small, energetic, bossy, and thinks he knows it all. He's like the sort of teacher who runs after you in the street for not wearing school socks. He has a hat with a feather in it that bobs up and down when he is angry.
SHERIFF	You! Cretin! What are your fabulous prizes?
RABIES	Erm . . . A fabulous box of mud, twelve fabulous bottles of mud, and a fortnight's holiday for two.
SHERIFF	Where?
RABIES	In some mud.
SHERIFF	Mmmm . . . not bad!
NARRATOR 2	The Sheriff tears off a ticket.
BARRINGTON	This man is the Sheriff of Nottingham.
NARRATOR 2	The Sheriff tears off a great handful of tickets.
BARRINGTON	And he works for the Bad King John. He's a liar, he's a spyer, he's a tricker and a nicker . . .
NARRATOR 2	The Sheriff walks away without paying for the tickets.
BARRINGTON	And he knows what's going on . . .

SHERIFF	I know what's going on. (*exits*)
BARRINGTON	But even though they're poor and sore The people have a dream One day someone will come along Who'll turn their mud to cream Someone who'll fight for the people's rights And set all the people free Who'll whip the Sheriff and Bad King John But who will this someone be?
NARRATOR 1	Marian enters.
MARIAN	I think he means me. With my ruthless band of freedom fighters.
	(*trumpet flourish*)
BARRINGTON	Now who will this someone be?

Scene 2: Worksop village

(NARRATORS 1 and 2, SHERIFF, RABIES and GARY)

NARRATOR 2	The Sheriff comes out of a tumble down hut with a boutique sign on it.
SHERIFF	And when you've finished them, sew on the Royal Coat of Arms.
RABIES	Excuse me, my Lord. (*holding out a hand for money*)
SHERIFF	(*calling into the hut*) I'll be back in ten minutes, so make sure they're ready.

RABIES My Lord?

SHERIFF Go away!

RABIES Remember me, my Lord?

SHERIFF No, I never met you before in my life. If I had, I'd have chopped your face off for polluting the environment.

RABIES But what about my raffle?

SHERIFF What raffle?

RABIES The raffle what you took all the tickets for.

SHERIFF You're running a raffle?

RABIES Yes.

SHERIFF Then where's your licence?

RABIES What licence?

SHERIFF Guards!

NARRATOR 1 Enter Gary and Graeme, two very large and very dim Norman guards.

GARY Hullo!

SHERIFF (*to guards*) I'm arresting this man for being in possession of a raffle without a licence. And I'm confiscating all his prizes. This village needs cleaning up!
(*aside*) And what's more, Mrs Nottingham and I could do with a nice holiday for two.

Scene 3: In front of a peasant's hut

(NARRATORS 1 and 2, BARRINGTON, OLD LADY and SHERIFF)

NARRATOR 2 An old lady peasant is sitting in front of some muddy washing.

BARRINGTON (*furtively*) Hey Gladys man, you hungry?

OLD LADY Barrington, I'm always hungry.

BARRINGTON D'you wanna buy some rats?

OLD LADY (*she becomes equally furtive*) Rats! Wicked! Let's have a look.

NARRATOR 2 Barrington opens his coat to reveal several rows of rats of all sizes pinned to the inside.

BARRINGTON What flavour d'you want? I've got cheese and onion, salt and vinegar, prawn cocktail. And this little fellow's new on the market – barbequed chicken with cream cheese and chives.

NARRATOR 1 The Sheriff bursts on to the scene from behind the washing.

SHERIFF Got you, sunshine!
You are nicked!

BARRINGTON What do you mean, man. I haven't done nuffink.

SHERIFF There is a 'sell-by' date stamped on the bottom of that rat; what's it say Barrington?

BARRINGTON (*reads*) 16th July, 1195.

SHERIFF — And what's today, Barrington?

BARRINGTON — 17th July, 1195.

SHERIFF — So you're selling foul, stinking, rotten mouldy goods to innocent little old ladies, aren't you, son? It's the stocks for you my lad! Followed by a nice little trial up at Nottingham Castle. Guards!

NARRATOR 2 — Barrington is dragged away to join Rabies in the stocks. The peasants look on, silently disapproving.

Scene 4: A bridge across a small river in the forest

(NARRATORS 1 and 2, MARIAN, EDWINA and LITTLE RON)

NARRATOR 2 — Someone is coming through the undergrowth carrying a large barrel full of water, which she spills and slops as she goes along. She grunts with the effort of her heavy load. It is, of course, our heroine.

MARIAN — It's hard to say goodbye, old friend. I taught you to fetch and carry, sit up and beg. I knitted you a little hat, I made you a coat out of kipper skins, and ballet shoes from a weasel's thigh-bone. But now I'm so poor I can no longer afford to keep you. Farewell, Edwina.

EDWINA — Brddip-up!

A VOICE — Halt!

NARRATOR 1	Marian is about to cross the bridge. In front of her is a fierce man with an ear-ring, a long thick staff and a big black beard. He is three feet tall.
LITTLE RON	There's no room on this bridge for the both of us. Stand aside stranger, or I, Little Ron, will knock you into the water.
MARIAN	Pardon?
LITTLE RON	See what a lusty staff I have, the very thing for cracking the pates of insolent rogues.
NARRATOR 2	Marian peers round the barrel. She is seventeen, dumpy, with a wild shock of hair in which are little plaits with ribbons.
MARIAN	Look, I don't want to be rude, Mr Ron, but it's a very large bridge, and quite frankly you're not exactly massive, are you? I'm quite sure you could squeeze past if you wanted to.
LITTLE RON	We'll fight here on the bridge, so if one of us goes in the water, there'll be no doubt who has won, and the victor may go on their way without a wetting.
MARIAN	(*putting down the barrel*) And that's what you want?
LITTLE RON	Aye!
MARIAN	(*rolling up her sleeves*) We can't just sit down and talk about it?

LITTLE RON Nay!

MARIAN OK. Have it your way.

NARRATOR 2 Ron roars and swings at Marian. She ducks and he hurtles into the water.

MARIAN (*peering over the edge of the bridge*) Are you all right?

NARRATOR 1 Ron stands in the water laughing like a maniac. He's been beaten but he's had a good fight. There is a little noise from the barrel.

EDWINA Brrdid-up!

MARIAN There, there, Edwina, don't cry. I'll find you a good home. Come on. (*she exits*)

Scene 5: Worksop village

(NARRATORS 1 and 2, SHERIFF, MARIAN, ROBIN, EDWINA, GRAEME and GARY)

NARRATOR 2 Splaatt! A rotten tomato hits Rabies full in the face as he sits imprisoned in the stocks. The Sheriff roars with triumph. He turns to peasants who are standing sullenly behind him in little groups.

SHERIFF Bullseye!!! What a shot, eh? Ha-ha-ha!!

NARRATOR 1 Rabies scoops the tomato remnants off his face with his tongue as he realises it's the best meal he's had for months.

SHERIFF Wasn't that brilliant? Wasn't it funny? Wasn't it the most hysterically humorous thing you've ever seen in your entire lives?

NARRATOR 2 The peasants are totally unamused.

SHERIFF Now listen to me you disgusting bunch of doughnut heads; throwing a tomato in someone's face is a hysterically funny joke actually, and anyone who doesn't think so is so stupid, so incredibly thick, that they'll be hung up by their toes, coated in chocolate spread and covered in a ravenously hungry swarm of killer wasps – Now laugh!

NARRATOR 1 The peasants look round uneasily. Nervously and without enthusiasm they begin to laugh. Rabies beams happily and laughs with them. Barrington raises his eyes to heaven. From out of the forest Marian enters the clearing.

MARIAN We're here Edwina – Worksop market. Now for the hard sell.
Roll up! Roll up! Fantastic bargain at a ludicrous price. Buy now while stock lasts!

NARRATOR 2 Marian is revelling in the role of being a market trader but there is no one in sight. She peers into a hut. From out of the next hut Robin emerges. He is handsome in a medallion man sort of way, but he is a complete idiot. He finishes folding something large, white, soft and woolly. He looks round nervously for the Sheriff. Marian dips her hand in the water, scoops up Edwina and rushes up to him.

MARIAN Excuse me, Sir, you look like a man who knows a good thing when he sees one.

ROBIN Yuh, well I *am* a pretty smart cookie, I must admit, you know.

MARIAN In my hand I've got a bargain, and I do mean a bargain. It's this year's model, it's got a three year guarantee and it's made in Britain. What d'you think?

NARRATOR 2 Robin looks interested but pretends not to be.

ROBIN (*with mock indifference*) Mmmmm.

MARIAN And if you can find a cheaper one anywhere in the whole of Sherwood we'll refund your money.

ROBIN (*he's definitely interested now*) Really?

MARIAN You want to see?

ROBIN Umm. Yah. OK.

NARRATOR 1 Robin's head bends curiously forward as Marian raises her hand and opens it.

EDWINA Brrdid-up!

NARRATOR 2 Robin squawks with fear, flailing the air with the woolly thing as though he has been attacked by a wasp.

ROBIN Aaagghh!! It's alive. It's attacking me! Take it away!

MARIAN Don't be silly. It's only a tadpole.

ROBIN No it isn't. It stung me! I can feel it! Get me a bandage! Take me to casualty!

MARIAN Look, it's in my hand, it never left my hand and tadpoles can't sting.

ROBIN (*slumping down onto log*) Yuh, yuh, you're right of course. I'm sorry, it's the pressure. The job's really getting to me, you know.

MARIAN What job?

ROBIN Well . . . (*vainly attempting to appear modest*) I've been commissioned to run up a little something for the Royal Household; I mean, I say a little something, but it's got to be absolutely . . . you know, I mean, I think royalty are great, don't you? They're so natural and . . . I don't know, cred. That King John, he's a real . . .

MARIAN Fat slob?

ROBIN No, he's sharp, tasteful – he knows what he wants and he goes out and gets it. He knows there's only one *really* trendy tailor in the whole of Sherwood, so he said, you know, go for it – and here they are.

NARRATOR 2 Robin holds up a vast pair of underpants emblazoned with the royal crest.

MARIAN Those! Those great dishcloths! That's what you're so proud of! You jerk! There's peasants starving to death out there while you get rich making enormous pairs of pants for the royal bottom. Come on Edwina, I promised you a good master, not a traitor.

NARRATOR 1 Marian dumps Edwina back in the barrel. She sees the small crowd.

MARIAN Let's try *them*.

SHERIFF (*to crowd*) And now I will attempt the one-handed curved tomato throw with double somersault and pike. Stand by to applaud, please. (*he winds himself up*)

MARIAN Tadpole! Tadpole! Lovely fresh tadpole! Who'll buy my . . .

NARRATOR 2 Marian crosses between the Sheriff and the stocks and splatt! The tomato hits her full in the face.

MARIAN Right, who did that? Who was it?

SHERIFF (*venomously*) It was me, actually.

MARIAN Oh it was you, actually, was it? Well it wasn't very funny.

SHERIFF Yes it was. It was incredibly funny.

MARIAN You nasty little stoat!

NARRATOR 2 In a blind fury Marian flings the barrel of water at the Sheriff. Splash. The Sheriff is

	knocked to the ground. The crowd goes wild.
MARIAN	Oh, no! Edwina! What have I done!
EDWINA	Brrdid-up!
MARIAN	You've swallowed her! You horrible brute! You've swallowed Edwina!
NARRATOR 1	The Sheriff rolls his eyes and tries to talk with a tadpole stuck in his throat.
MARIAN	Don't worry darling, I'll save you.
NARRATOR 2	Marian races over to the Sheriff and proceeds to give his stomach violent artificial respiration. The Sheriff's head pounds up and down on the ground. In the stocks, Rabies and Barrington are enjoying the scene.
NARRATOR 1	The guards, thinking Marian fancies the Sheriff, smile on indulgently.
NARRATOR 2	Marian open the Sheriff's mouth and shouts down his throat.
MARIAN	This way darling! This way!
NARRATOR 1	Marian sits firmly on the Sheriff's stomach.
NARRATOR 2	The guards nudge each other coyly.
SHERIFF	Aaaagghh!
NARRATOR 1	The tadpole shoots out of his mouth like a bullet from a gun, and splot! goes straight up Rabies' nose.

EDWINA Brrdid-up!

NARRATOR 2 Rabies looks surprised.

MARIAN Edwina!

NARRATOR 1 Marian jumps off the Sheriff and races towards the stocks.

SHERIFF (*dazed but angry*) Guards, arrest that woman!

GRAEME But she loves you, sire. She called you darling and everything.

SHERIFF Get her!

NARRATOR 1 Graeme runs after her. Gary tries to draw his sword, but it's stuck in his scabbard. Vainly he tries to pull it out.

MARIAN Whooaah!

NARRATOR 2 Marian veers off into the crowd and dives between the legs of the crowd of peasants. Graeme follows. The crowd bobs up and down as two unseen objects pass between their legs.

SHERIFF Kill her!

NARRATOR 1 Marian finally appears between Gary's legs.

MARIAN Having trouble?

GARY It's stuck.

MARIAN Don't worry.

NARRATOR 2	Marian grasps the sword hilt, puts a foot in Gary's stomach and heaves. Gary topples over backwards. Marian now has a sword. Graeme re-appears growling, and he and the Sheriff edge towards Marian.
SHERIFF	(*menacingly*) So the cross little girly-whirly wants to fight, does she? Well that's all right by me. I've got a black belt in sword fighting, a distinction in my dagger proficiency test and what is more, I cheat. (*he laughs*)
NARRATOR 1	Graeme laughs.
NARRATOR 2	Marian looks from left to right. How can she escape?
SHERIFF	Prepare to be turned into dog food.
NARRATOR 1	Suddenly Marian lunges into the crowd, grabs the boutique keeper and holds the sword to his throat.
MARIAN	Stop! One false move and I'll run this man through.
SHERIFF	(*sarcastically*) Oh goodness me! What a terrible threat! Let's all put our weapons back in their cases and go home, shall we? Are you mad? Do you think I have the slightest interest in that worm's life? I've seen more interesting faces on the wrong end of a donkey. (*to the guards*) Guards! Kill her, and if he gets in the way hack him to pieces.

NARRATOR 2 They start to move.

MARIAN I said stop! Do you see what he has in his hands – King John's underpants. If he gets run through, what'll happen to them? Great, big, red stains, and have you ever tried getting blood out of weasel wool? It's impossible!

GRAEME (*to Sheriff*) She's right sir! I tried it with my usual washing powder and the stains just wouldn't shift.

SHERIFF All right! All right! All right! Let them go!

NARRATOR 1 The crowd parts. Marian and Robin exit.

SHERIFF (*quietly*) But Graeme ... ambush them at the crossroads.

Scene 6: The chase

(NARRATORS 1 and 2, BARRINGTON, MARIAN, ROBIN and GRAEME)

BARRINGTON (*rapping*)
So Marian flees to the wild old wood
And her hostage flees there too
She may have a man, but she ain't got a plan
What's the poor girl going to do?

NARRATOR 1 Marian is exhausted, largely because she's giving Robin a piggy-back.

BARRINGTON	'Cos that man is a real liability.
NARRATOR 2	The cross roads are apparently deserted. Enter Marian, hot and panting, with Robin on her back.
MARIAN	Right! We're safe here. Thanks very much. You can walk back now.
NARRATOR 1	Marian dumps him by a tree and he fans himself with his pants. Suddenly, two mailed hands reach out of the bushes and snatch the pants from him.
ROBIN	(*in fury*) Get your hands off my underpants!
NARRATOR 2	Robin snatches them back, then pulls off one of his assailant's mailed gloves and flails about with it behind the trees. Out topples Gary, pole-axed. Robin is mortified and attempts to bring him round by slapping his face.
ROBIN	Sorry! Oh wow, I'm sorry!
NARRATOR 1	Robin looks up. Standing over him is an irate Graeme. His slaps turn to nervous little pats.
ROBIN	I didn't mean to hurt him.
GRAEME	Oh no, you didn't mean to hurt him. You only hit him in the face with a glove – very hard – when he didn't even have his sword . . . Bully!

NARRATOR 2	Robin turns and races down a path. Marian races after him and turns him round. He has gone down the wrong path. They flee.

Scene 7: The bridge

(LITTLE RON, MARIAN, NARRATORS 1 and 2)

LITTLE RON	Halt! There's no room on this bridge for both of us.
MARIAN	(*under her breath*) Oh, no!
LITTLE RON	Stand aside stranger, or I, Little Ron, will knock you into the water.
ROBIN	(*politely*) Would you mind holding on a moment . . . (*to Marian*) What shall I do?
MARIAN	(*quietly*) Knock him into the water.
ROBIN	But I can't handle violence.
MARIAN	Well that's a pity, 'cos there are two enormous blood-thirsty Normans just about to come round that bend, and they just love it.
ROBIN	Ah! Right! See what you mean. Never let it be said that I, Robin of Islington, refused a challenge. Let the fight commence!
NARRATOR 1	Ron roars, then knocks Robin straight into the water.
MARIAN	Oh great!

NARRATOR 2 — She crosses the bridge and looks wearily at Little Ron.

MARIAN — It doesn't prove anything you know.

NARRATOR 1 — Marian looks back across the other side of the river and sees two helmets and two raised swords above the bushes bobbing up and down as they get nearer.

MARIAN — Mind you, there's two massive great blokes back there who are simply dying for a fight – *and* they've got swords and daggers. Beating them would be something, wouldn't it?

NARRATOR 2 — Little Ron nods, his eyes shining with anticipation. Marian wades into the water and begins to pull out a bedraggled weed-covered Robin.

MARIAN — Come on, Robin of Islington!

Scene 8: Nottingham castle

(NARRATORS 1 and 2, SHERIFF, KING JOHN, BARRINGTON and RABIES)

NARRATOR 1 — Meanwhile in Nottingham Castle . . .

NARRATOR 2 — Quaking peasants are queueing in a castle corridor. At the head of the queue are Barrington and Rabies in chains, by a seriously heavy door bearing the notice 'King John's Study'.

SHERIFF (*from inside the study*) Next!

NARRATOR 1 Barrington and Rabies enter. The study is smoky, gloomy and full of terror.

NARRATOR 2 King John sits behind a desk like a huge, warty toad with long hair and a crown on his head. The Sheriff stands at his shoulder.

NARRATOR 1 King John laughs, relishing the imminent destruction of the two innocents.

KING JOHN Mmnaa! Mmnaa!

BARRINGTON (*cheerily*) Mornin!

NARRATOR 2 Rabies waves to the king in a friendly fashion.

KING JOHN (*really enjoying himself*) And why have you been brought before me, you worthless creature?

BARRINGTON (*pointing to the Sheriff*) He arrested me.

SHERIFF He arrested me, *Your Majesty*.

BARRINGTON He arrested me, Your Majesty.

KING JOHN And of what are you accused?

BARRINGTON Selling a rat, answering back, whistling in the corridor and dumb insolence.

KING JOHN Then I find you guilty. Mmnh! Mmnh! (*he laughs*)

BARRINGTON Thanks very much.

KING JOHN	And I sentence you to five hundred lines and a month's torture.
BARRINGTON	I hate lines.
KING JOHN	(*referring to Rabies*) And what about that disgusting object?
SHERIFF	Illegal gambling, obtaining money under false pretences and being incredibly stupid.
KING JOHN	Guilty! (*he laughs*) Mmnh! Mmnh! And have you anything to say?
RABIES	Mnnaa! Mmnh! Mmnh!
KING JOHN	(*outraged*) What?
RABIES	(*insistently*) Mnnaa! Mnnaa! Mnnaa!
SHERIFF	Quiet, dog! Would you mock our beloved sovereign?
RABIES	(*protesting his innocence*) Mnnaa! Mnnaa! Mnnaa! Mnnaa!
BARRINGTON	(*to Sheriff*) He says you'd sound like him (*points to King John*) if you had a tadpole stuck up your nose.
KING JOHN	Foul insolence! I will punish you both as no man has ever been punished before. I will do such disgusting things to you that even the torturers will go 'urggh!' and ask to leave the room.
BARRINGTON	(*aside*) One thing I'll say about British justice. You always get a fair trial.

Scene 9: A forest glade

(MARIAN, ROBIN, NARRATORS 1 and 2)

MARIAN (*thoughtfully*) Robin. Robin! . . . Robin!!!

ROBIN Are they coming?

MARIAN No.

ROBIN Have they gone?

MARIAN Yes.

ROBIN Then can I go home?

MARIAN Home! Home! We've spent all morning clobbering Normans. You'll never be able to go home again.

NARRATOR 1 Robin's face slowly crumples. Is that a tear we see?

MARIAN From now on, we'll have to live here in the forest.

ROBIN What, buy a holiday cottage?

MARIAN No Robin, we'll camp out under the stars.

ROBIN But I haven't brought my wellingtons.

MARIAN We'll make bows and arrows and we'll hold rich travellers to ransom.

ROBIN (*suddenly interested*) Oh what, money d'you mean?

MARIAN Yes, and we'll give it all to the poor.

ROBIN I wanna go home!!!

NARRATOR 2	Marian leaps off into the middle of the glade. She is in the grip of a beautiful vision.
MARIAN	And we'll surround ourselves with a band of highly attractive, respectable young men who are just a *little* bit rough and . . . are dedicated to freeing our country from tyranny and injustice and . . . and . . . cruelty to animals and stuff . . . and we'll swing through the trees on long ropes, and we'll have our own costumes . . . and we'll never be cross or grumpy, and we'll do these fantastically brave deeds with a merry smile on our faces. And everyone will say 'Good heavens, it's those Merry Men, come in and have a cup of tea; can we have your autograph?' And no one will dare stand against us. And our names will go down in history, and we'll be famous for ever and people will name pubs after us. What do you think?
ROBIN	(*pause*) We'll really have our own costumes?
MARIAN	Yes.
ROBIN	Originals, I mean, not out of a catalogue?
MARIAN	Yes.
ROBIN	Who's going to design them?
MARIAN	You?

ROBIN (*pause*) Right – you're on. (*they shake hands excitedly*) I'll have to do some drawings, of course, but I think *flared* trousers, well when I say flares, I don't mean, you know, 'flares', more a bit of fullness in the lower leg . . .

MARIAN The clobber must wait till tomorrow, Robin. First, we must go to the aid of a tadpole in distress. Forward to Nottingham Castle.

Scene 10: Another part of the forest

(ROBIN, MARIAN and NARRATOR 1)

NARRATOR 1 In the distance we can see Marian and Robin, with Robin constantly turning back, Marian returning to fetch him and dragging him onwards.

ROBIN . . . and we'll have waisted jackets, with narrow . . . you know . . . and square round the . . . and we'll have studs, big chunky studs, and – oh, that reminds me – it's Wednesday, the shops shut at one – you go on and I'll nip back to the stud shop.

MARIAN It's Thursday – come on!

ROBIN Right! Thursday! OK! . . . and we'll have suede stitching – and a leather label, and rivets on the . . . oh, no! Rivets. I haven't got any rivets. Stupid me! Won't be long.

MARIAN You can get rivets in Nottingham.

ROBIN Nottingham! . . . Yah! . . . You're right, absolutely! (*he falls flat on the ground*) Oooh! It's gone!

MARIAN What's gone?

ROBIN Ligament. Completely gone. What a drag. It's always the same. One minute right as rain, then bang!, just like that. Don't worry though, it's not a problem. A few days with my feet up, I'll be as right as rain.

MARIAN Robin, there's nothing wrong with your ligament that won't be cured by me kicking it. Now get up . . . Come on.
What's the matter?

ROBIN Nothing . . . nothing . . . We're just going to get killed, that's all.

MARIAN No we're not. We're going to be heroes.

ROBIN Yes, dead heroes. And for why? I'll tell you for why. One, there's only two of us. Two, one of us is a coward and three, as soon as we get to Nottingham we'll be chopped to bits.

NARRATOR 1 They are approaching the bridge.

Scene 11: At the bridge

(MARIAN, LITTLE RON, NARRATORS 1 and 2, GRAEME, GARY and ROBIN)

MARIAN — That's rubbish, Robin. Everything's going to go smoothly. Trust me.

LITTLE RON — Halt!

NARRATOR 1 — You guessed it! Little Ron is on the bridge.

LITTLE RON — There's no room on this bridge for the both of us!

MARIAN — (*aside*) I don't believe this! (*politely to Little Ron*) Now look, I don't want to get aggressive, but we're dreadfully busy, we've got a tadpole to rescue and I'm afraid if you don't get out of the way I'm going to have to lose my temper.

NARRATOR 2 — Graeme and Gary, dripping and battered, are up to their necks in the river. Their helmets have gone, but they are still in their chain mail hoods.

NARRATOR 1 — Graeme begins to clamber out on to the bank.

GRAEME — No don't, whatever you do. He'll tear you to pieces. The man's an animal.

MARIAN — (*thinking*) Is he?

GARY — Yes, a crazed fighting machine.

MARIAN — Really? – oh good! Sounds like just the man we need. Little Ron, would you like to

join our gang of fearless outlaws who fight against injustice and do incredibly brave things like . . . getting their ears pierced and . . . tattooing themselves . . .
and . . . pulling their teeth out just for the fun of it.

LITTLE RON Oooh! Sounds just like my sort of thing.

MARIAN Right! Let's go. We've got a castle to break into.

ROBIN But how do we get there without being . . . you know.

MARIAN Recognised? I'm glad you asked me that. Guards! Take your clothes off.

NARRATOR 2 Graeme and Gary stand shivering on the bank.

GRAEME Pardon?

MARIAN Take your clothes off.

GARY No way. Sorry. Absolutely not.

MARIAN I'm going to count up to one. If your clothes aren't in a heap by my feet by the time I've finished counting, I'm going to order Little Ron to tear them off with his teeth.

NARRATOR 1 Little Ron happily bears his teeth and growls.

MARIAN One . . .

NARRATOR 2 Two piles of clothes drop at her feet.

MARIAN	Thank you, boys! (*drawing Robin and Little Ron into a huddle*) Right gang, now this is what we'll do . . .

Scene 12: Castle courtyard at night

(NARRATORS 1 and 2, GATEKEEPER, MARIAN, BARRINGTON, ROBIN, RABIES and LITTLE RON)

NARRATOR 1	Rap! Rap! Rap!
NARRATOR 2	A hand rattles a massive brass knocker that looks like a podgy dwarf. Inside the castle courtyard a burly, middle-aged Norman with a big boozy nose and a lantern looks through grille.
GATEKEEPER	All right! All right! I'm coming. Who is it at this time of night? You're not salesmen are you?
MARIAN	(*in a gruff voice*) No!
GATEKEEPER	Jehovah's Witnesses?
MARIAN	No!
GATEKEEPER	Then what do you want?
NARRATOR 1	The gatekeeper slides open an inspection window. Marian is wearing a chain mail hood which obscures her face.
MARIAN	Make way for the Royal underpants!
GATEKEEPER	Oh, ah! He's been waiting for them.
NARRATOR 2	The gatekeeper opens the heavy door. In

march Marian and Robin dressed as Normans. Marian carries the neatly folded pants. Robin, who is also obscured by a chain mail hood, looks extremely fat. They have just reached the centre of the courtyard when . . .

GATEKEEPER Wait a minute! I don't know you.

NARRATOR 1 He approaches, holding up the lantern.

GATEKEEPER Who are you?

NARRATOR 2 He inspects Robin with the lantern, starting with his face and moving downwards until he reaches his knees. Robin has four legs.

GATEKEEPER You've got too many feet!

NARRATOR 1 An arm shoots out of Robin's middle and a truncheon bangs the gatekeeper on the head. He groans and collapses on the flag-stones.

MARIAN Brilliant! You can come out now.

NARRATOR 2 Little Ron appears out of Robin's costume.

MARIAN Now where do we go? This place is huge!

BARRINGTON (*off*) Aargggghh!

NARRATOR 1 They look up at a turret in which flickers a feeble light.

MARIAN What was that?

LITTLE RON The agonised cry of a poor wretch undergoing terrible torture.

RABIES — (*off*) Mnnnaaaaaaaa!

ROBIN — And what was that?

LITTLE RON — The agonised cry of a poor wretch undergoing terrible torture with a tadpole up his nose.

MARIAN — Edwina! Come on!

NARRATOR 1 — Marian and Little Ron race off. Robin looks terrified. Marian races back.

MARIAN — Come *on*!!

NARRATOR 2 — She drags Robin off with her.

Scene 13: King John's study

(NARRATORS 1 and 2, SHERIFF and KING JOHN)

NARRATOR 1 — The Sheriff and King John have come to the end of the queue.

SHERIFF — ... and finally your Royal Highness, this one.

NARRATOR 2 — A particularly rough, huge and surly soldier steps forward.

SHERIFF — Bullying, shouting, swearing, kicking kittens, and stealing children's sweets.

KING JOHN — Well done, corporal. You're just the sort of man we need in today's army. I'm making you sergeant. Well, that's enough business for today – now, Mnnaaa! ... pleasure.

SHERIFF — To the torture chamber?

KING JOHN	To the torture chamber. (*they exit*)

Scene 14: The castle dungeon

(NARRATORS 1 and 2)

NARRATOR 1	Our heroes arrive at a huge cell door. There are screams of agony within. Little Ron hurls himself at the door, smashes through the bottom quarter and disappears inside. Marian raises her eyebrows, opens the door, and she and Robin walk in. The door closes.
NARRATOR 2	Our heroes see the agonised face of Barrington, sweat dripping from his forehead.
NARRATOR 1	They see the agonised face of Rabies.
NARRATOR 2	They are looking at something terrible.
NARRATOR 1	Lit by a flickering torch is a little mouse on a treadmill. The treadmill is operating two pairs of sticks with feathers on the end. Barrington and Rabies are hanging from the wall by chains – the feathers are tickling their feet.
NARRATOR 2	Then the door bursts open. It is King John and the Sheriff.
NARRATOR 1	Bang! They are knocked on the head. The room spins round and round.

Scene 15: The castle dungeon

(NARRATORS 1 and 2, MARIAN, ROBIN, SHERIFF, KING JOHN and BARRINGTON)

NARRATOR 1	The Sheriff and King John are now hanging from the wall and Marian is arranging the tickling sticks under their feet.
MARIAN	And now see how honest freedom fighters treat the forces of evil. You will suffer the same punishment you meted out to others.
ROBIN	Yes – you'll be imprisoned, tortured and what is more . . .
NARRATOR 2	Robin flings back his hood dramatically and snatches the blazing torch.
ROBIN	See! I set fire to your underpants!
SHERIFF	Wait a minute! I know you, don't I?
MARIAN	Robin! Hood!
NARRATOR 1	Quickly Robin pulls the hood back over his face.
BARRINGTON	Goodbye! Sorry we couldn't hang around.
NARRATOR 2	Barrington starts the tickling machine and exits with Rabies, Marian, Robin and Little Ron.
SHERIFF	I'll revenge myself on them if it's the last thing I do.
KING JOHN	I'll leave the riff-raff to you. I want their leader. Nobody burns my underpants and

	gets away with it. What did they call him... Robin Hood?
SHERIFF	Yes... Robin Hood.
NARRATOR 1	The Sheriff begins to laugh... the tickling sticks are doing their job. King John glares at him, then he too is forced to laugh.

Scene 16: A forest glade at night

(NARRATOR 1, MARIAN, BARRINGTON, RABIES and GOSPEL CHOIR)

NARRATOR 1	Our heroes are sitting round a campfire.
MARIAN	...and I solemnly swear...
BARRINGTON	...and I solemnly swear...
MARIAN	...to fight injustice...
BARRINGTON	...to fight injustice...
MARIAN	...and to do a good deed everyday.
BARRINGTON	...and to do a good deed everyday.
MARIAN	Cross my heart and hope to die, stick a sausage in my eye!
BARRINGTON	Cross my heart and hope to die, stick a sausage in my eye!
MARIAN	Now you, Rabies. I, Rabies...
RABIES	(*solemnly swearing his oath*) Mnnaa Mnnaa – nnaa...

MARIAN Wishing to be a Merry Man . . .

RABIES Mnaa-naa naa naa naa Mnaa-naa Mnaa . . .

MARIAN Do swear to wear the uniform and keep it clean . . .

RABIES Mnna-naa naa . . . (*his eyes bulge. He is about to sneeze*) Mnaa! Mnaa! (*he points to his nose alarmed*)

MARIAN What?

RABIES Mnaa! Mnaa! Mnaa!

MARIAN You're going to sneeze? Well go ahead.

RABIES Mnaa-naa, Mnaa-naa Mnaa Mnaa.

MARIAN You haven't got a hanky? Well that doesn't matter – we're free now. What need we Merry Men of hankies? We can sneeze where we like. Into leaves, into grass – why, even into this blazing fire.

RABIES Mnaa Mnaa Mnaa-naa Mnaa-naa naa naa Mnaa?

MARIAN Yes, Rabies, even though you've got a tadpole up your . . . No! Rabies! Please don't sneeze.

RABIES Ahh . . . Shoo!!

NARRATOR 1 Marian looks appalled as Rabies sneezes into the fire. Suddenly a gospel choir starts up:

GOSPEL CHOIR *Marian's Song*

Marian –
Why don't you carry on
With what you're doing
'Cos there's always trouble brewing
Gotta find a way
To make a better day
Wow! Wow! Marian
Wow! Wow! Wow! Marian

Marian –
Why don't you carry on
With your Merry Men
And make heroes out of each of them
Gotta find a place
To make a better space
Wow! Wow! Marian
Wow! Wow! Wow! Marian

Drama activities

1 Try staging one or two short scenes from the play. These are the things you'll need to do:

- Choose the cast.
- Decide what the characters are like. Look for clues in the script about their age, appearance, the sort of person they are and how they behave to the other characters. Try not to copy other characters you have seen on film and television programmes.
- Work out how you will stage the play with the minimum of props.
- Rehearse the scene several times, and then perform it.

Here are some scenes to try out, together with the characters you'll need:

- Scene 2, pages 6–7;
- Scene 9, pages 25–27;
- Scene 11, pages 29–31.

2 Here are the titles of some new episodes of *Maid Marian and Her Merry Men*:

Nottingham Castle Fete
(The Sheriff organises a fete in his garden – Marian and Her Merry Men turn up to spoil the fun)

Mud Tax Collection Day
(The Sheriff tries to collect a mud tax from everyone – Marian and Her Merry Men capture a share of the profits)

Choose one of these, or, if you like, make up your own title.

- First discuss what happens in your episode. Where is it set? Who is in it? How does it begin? What happens? How does it end?
- Next, as a group, set up three still pictures, (like 'freeze frames' from a video), which show the important moments from the episode you have made up.

- Each person in the group plays a character, and no words or movements are allowed. You can change which characters you are in each of the 'freeze frames'.
- Now chose a title for each picture; one of the characters can speak to introduce it.
- Practise going from one still picture to the next as smoothly as you can, including your spoken titles as each picture 'freezes'.
- Prepare your pictures for about fifteen minutes, and then each group shows their three 'freeze frames' to the rest of the class.

Writing and talking about the play

1 This play is very funny. The humour comes from many sources. Sometimes it's just the words the characters say: clever insults; witty use of language. Sometimes it's the characters themselves, and sometimes the action and situation the characters find themselves in – or a combination of the LANGUAGE, CHARACTER and ACTION/SITUATION.

Look at pages 18–19 of Scene 5 beginning at the Sheriff's speech: 'So the cross little girly-whirly. . . ' and look carefully for the moments where Tony Robinson has aimed for humour. Each time you find some humour, try to work out how the humour is achieved.

When you have completed this, choose your favourite funny scene to write about in detail.

2 The language that the characters use in this play contains many elements of the way we speak today. The play, in theory, is set in the twelfth century. Imagine that you were asked to take a scene from the play and make it sound less late-twentieth-century. Look at Scene 9 (pages 25–27) and read from Marian's speech, 'From now on, we'll have to live in the forest' to the end of the scene.

Look closely for the language that you feel you would have to change and put it into either of the following categories:

MODERN CHATTY ENGLISH   MODERN IDEA   OTHER

Discuss your findings with others and think of some simple ways of changing *some* of the language you have found.

3 Working in a small group, think about the story of Robin Hood that you already knew before reading Maid Marian. Tony Robinson has used the characters, situations and ideas from the original story, and twisted them to make them funny.

Choose three of the characters that occur in both stories (or who have direct equivalents like Little Ron and Little John). For each one, discuss what is the same about the character and what is different. List your ideas about each character under the headings 'Robin Hood and His Merry Men' and 'Maid Marian and Her Merry Men'.

You can also add any features of the original story that have been retained in *Maid Marian* and any features of the original story that have been left out or changed.

Next choose another well-known legend or fairy tale that you know, like King Arthur, William Tell or Red Riding Hood. Working in your group or in a pair, re-write the story to make it funny for a modern audience.

4 Look at the following letter:

Dear Points of View,

I have recently been unfortunate enough to have watched, with my children, the opening episode of *Maid Marian and Her Merry Men* – 'How the Band Got Together'.

As far as I am concerned, the programme has no merits whatsoever and I shall forbid my children to watch any further episodes of it.

Why, oh why, do people tamper with well-known stories? What on earth can be achieved? Bring back *Robin Hood and His Merry Men* and all will be forgiven.

Yours faithfully,
A Disappointed Viewer

Write a suitable reply to this letter in which you try to put forward some of the merits of the programme.

5 Barrington is the balladeer in the play. Ballads are poems or songs that tell a story, and many ballads were written and sung about Robin Hood. One of them starts like this:

Come listen to me, you gallants so free,
   All you that love mirth for to hear,
And I will tell you of a bold outlaw,
   That lived in Nottinghamshire.

Notice how many syllables there are in each line, (roughly 10, 8, 10, 8, though the last line here only has 7 syllables) and where the rhyme comes (at the end of lines 2 and 4), and this will give you a pattern to write to. You can vary the rhymes and syllables in your own writing if you want to, but try to keep the same pattern in each verse that you write.

Now write a ballad to tell the Tale of Maid Marian that you have read in this play.

PUBLISHED BY BBC EDUCATIONAL PUBLISHING AND
LONGMAN GROUP LIMITED

BBC Educational Publishing
a division of
BBC Enterprises Limited
Woodlands
80 Wood Lane
London W12 OTT

Pearson Education Limited
Edinburgh Gate, Harlow,
Essex CM20 2JE, England
and Associated Companies
throughout the world.

This educational edition first published 1992
Thirteenth impression 2006

ISBN-10: 0-582-09554-9
ISBN-13: 978-0-582-09554-0

Printed in Malaysia, GPS